PLAY MISSION PRAISE 1

Instrumental arrangements

Christopher Norton

Marshall Pickering

An Imprint of HarperCollins*Publishers*

Marshall Pickering is an imprint of
HarperCollins*Religious*,
part of HarperCollins*Publishers*,
77-85 Fulham Palace Road,
Hammersmith, London W6 8JB

1 3 5 7 9 10 8 6 4 2

ISBN 0 551 02954 4

Music and text set by Barnes Music Engraving Limited,
East sussex, England

Printed and bound in Great Britain by
Scotprint Limited, Musselburgh, Edinburgh

A catalogue record for this book is available from the British Library

CONTENTS

All heaven declares

Words: Tricia Richards
Music: Noel Richards

MPC 14

All heaven declares

All heaven declares

Give thanks

Words and music: Henry Smith
Keyboard arrangement: David Peacock

MPC 170

Give thanks

Give thanks

Give thanks

Great is the Lord

MPC 199

Words and music: Steve McEwan

Great is the Lord

Lord, we trust in Your un-fail-ing love, for You a-lone are God e-ter-nal,

through-out earth and hea-ven a - bove.

last time only

Great is the Lord

Great is the Lord

Hosanna, hosanna

MPC 242

Words and music: Carl Tuttle

Lord, we lift up Your name, __ with hearts full of praise. _

Be ex-alt-ed, O __ Lord my God – ho - san-na, in the high - est.
Be ex-alt-ed, O __ Lord my God – glo-ry to the King of kings.

Hosanna, hosanna

Hosanna, hosanna

Jesus, we celebrate Your victory

MPC 387

Words and music: John Gibson

Je - sus, we re - joice You've set

us free, Je - sus, Your death has brought us life.

Jesus, we celebrate Your victory

So we're re - joic - ing___ in God's vic - to - ry,
and in His pre - sence our prob - lems dis - ap - pear,

D.C. al Fine

our hearts re - spond - ing to His love.___
our hearts re - spond - ing to His love.___

Jesus, we celebrate Your victory

Jesus, we celebrate Your victory

Words and music: © 1987 Kingsway's Thankyou Music, PO Box 75, Eastbourne, East Sussex BN23 6NW, UK. Used by permission

Lord, the light of Your love is shining

MPC 445

Words and music: Graham Kendrick

1 Lord, the light of Your love is shin-ing, in the midst of the dark-ness, shin-ing:
2 Lord, I come to Your awe-some pres-ence, from the sha-dows in-to Your ra-diance;
3 As we gaze on Your king-ly bright-ness so our fa-ces dis-play Your like-ness,

Je - sus, Light of the world, shine up - on__ us; set us free by the truth You now bring us —
by Your blood I may en - ter Your bright-ness: search me, try me, con - sume all my dark-ness —
ev - er chang - ing from glo - ry to glo - ry: mir - rored here, may our lives tell Your sto - ry —

shine on____ me, shine on____ me.

Lord, the light of Your love is shining

na - tions with grace and mer - cy; send forth Your word,_ Lord, and let there be

light!

last time

Lord, the light of Your love is shining

Lord, the light of Your love is shining

MISSION PRAISE

Mission Praise was originally compiled for the Mission England campaign in 1984, and was especially designed to appeal to the broad range of churches taking part in the campaign. Its tremendous popularity led to two further collections, *Mission Praise 2* (1987) and the *Mission Praise Supplement*. In 1990 came *Mission Praise Combined*, drawing on the best of all three books to produce a definitive collection for church worship.

Features:

- a broad selection of traditional hymns and modern songs, combining the best of the old with the best of the new

- the most comprehensive collection available, with a total of 798 items

- items suitable for both choirs and music groups

- a wide range of hardwearing editions including hardback, paperback and spiral bindings

New!

Sing Mission Praise - a collection of attractive new vocal arrangements for 55 of the most popular worship songs from *Mission Praise Combined*

Play Mission Praise 2 - the second book in a new series of instrumental arrangements for *Mission Praise Combined*

Mission Praise Combined is available in the following editions:

Words edition	ISBN 0 551 01979 4	(single copy)
	ISBN 0 551 01977 8	(25 copy pack)
Easy-to-read words edition	ISBN 0 551 02627 8	
Large Print words edition	ISBN 0 551 01978 6	
Music edition	ISBN 0 551 01986 7	(hardback)
Musicians' edition vol. 1	ISBN 0 551 02266 3	(spiral bound)
Musicians' edition vol. 2	ISBN 0 551 02267 1	(spiral bound)
Musicians' edition vol. 3	ISBN 0 551 02268 X	(spiral bound)
Sing Mission Praise	ISBN 0 551 04010 6	
Play Mission Praise 2	ISBN 0 551 02955 2	